OWL at the VET

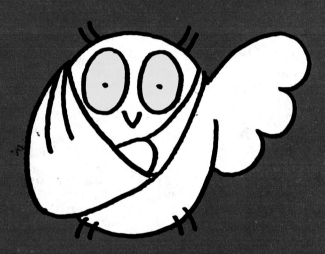

by Helen Nicoll
and Jan Pieńkowski

TED SMART

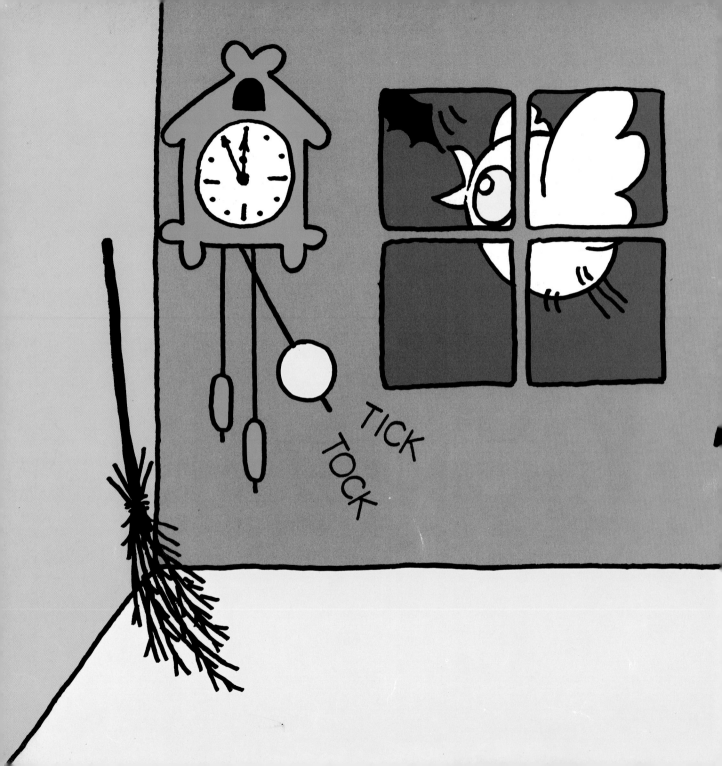

TICK
TOCK

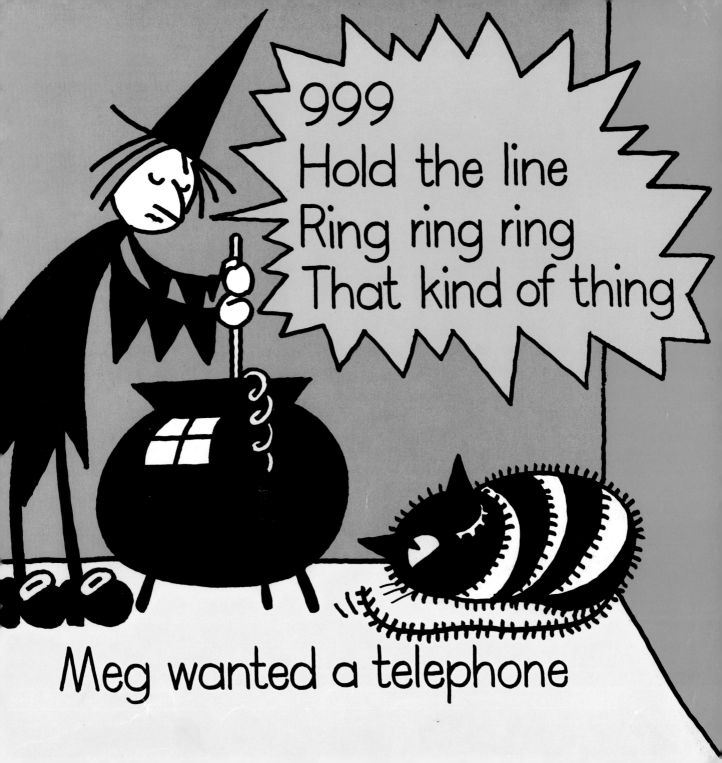

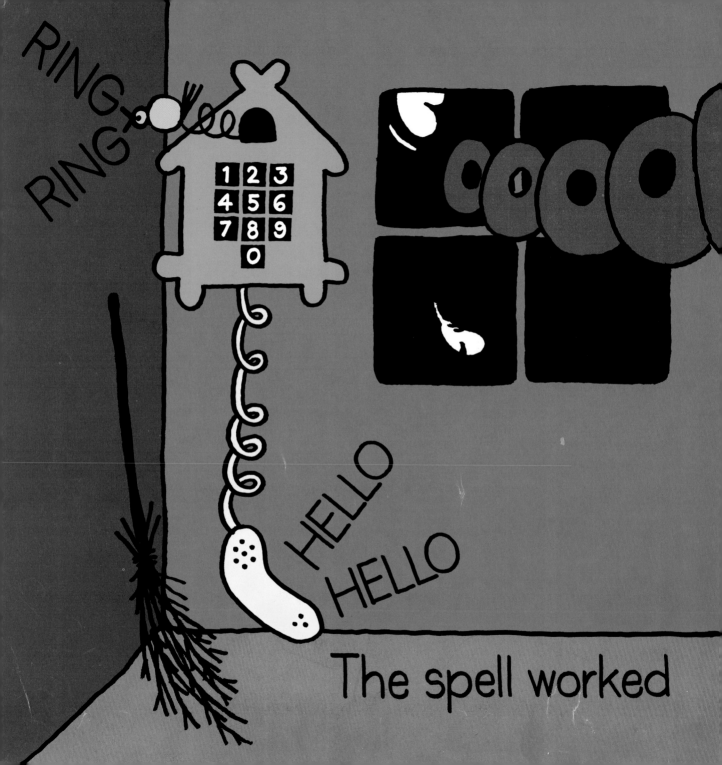

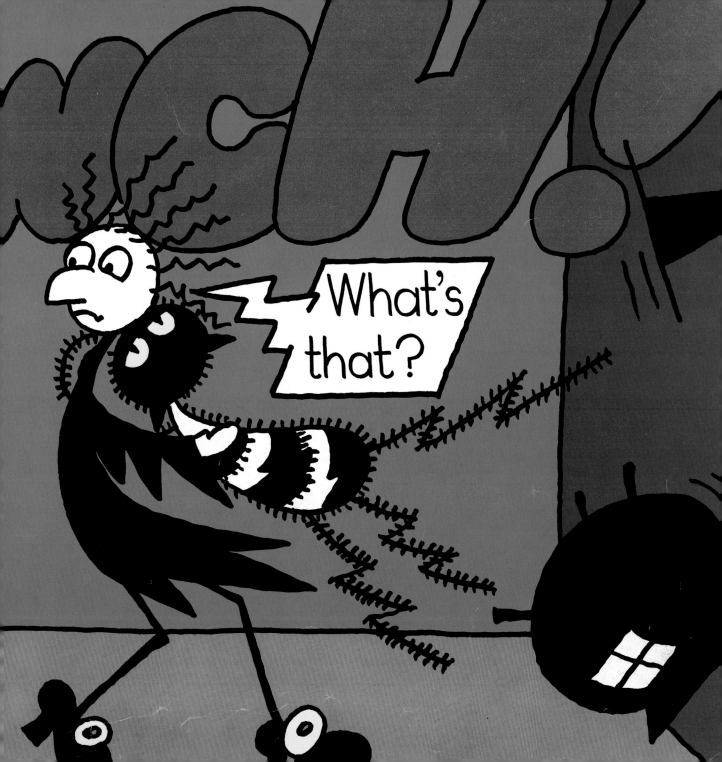

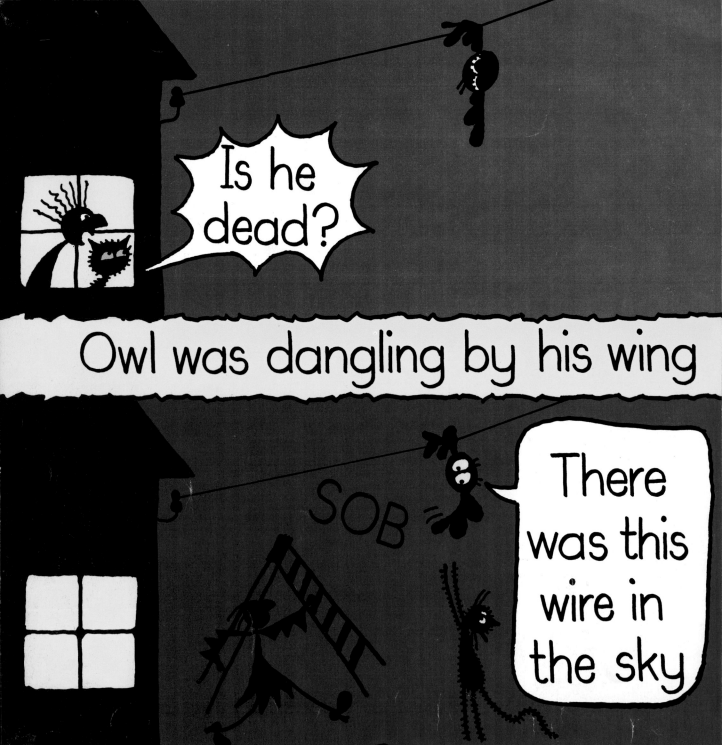

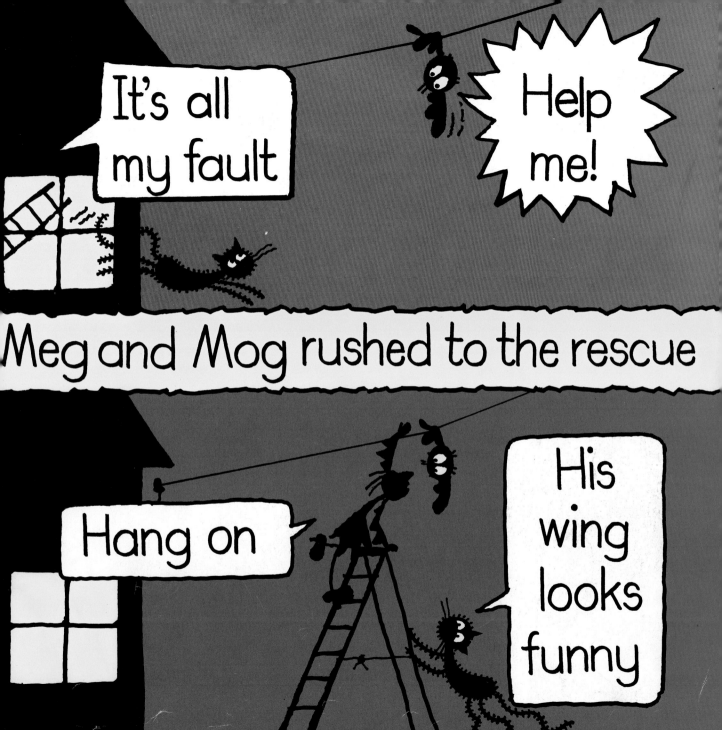

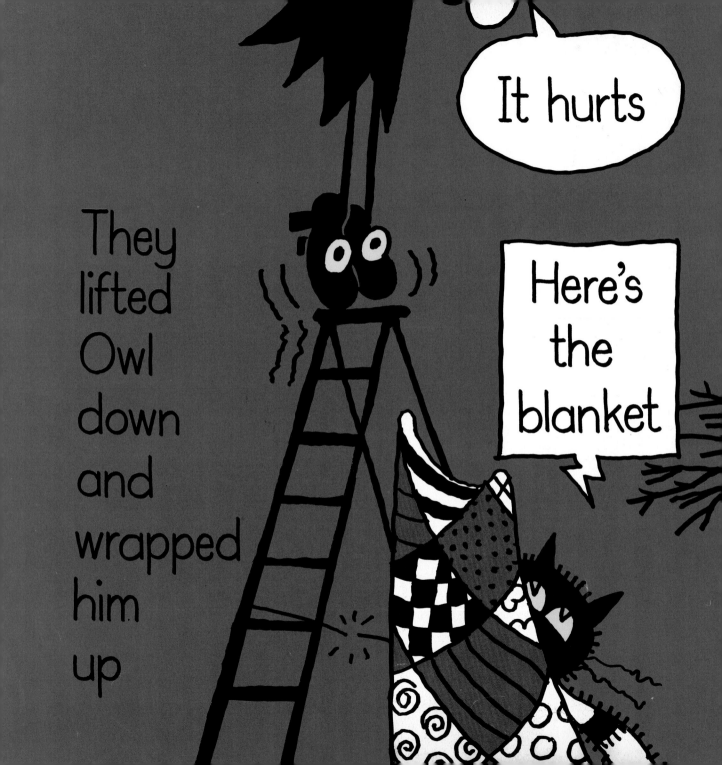

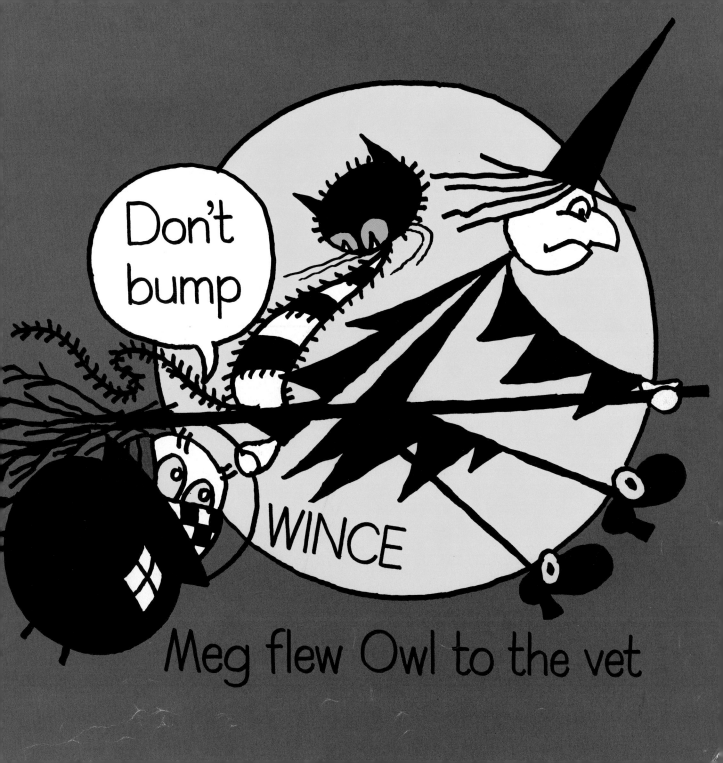

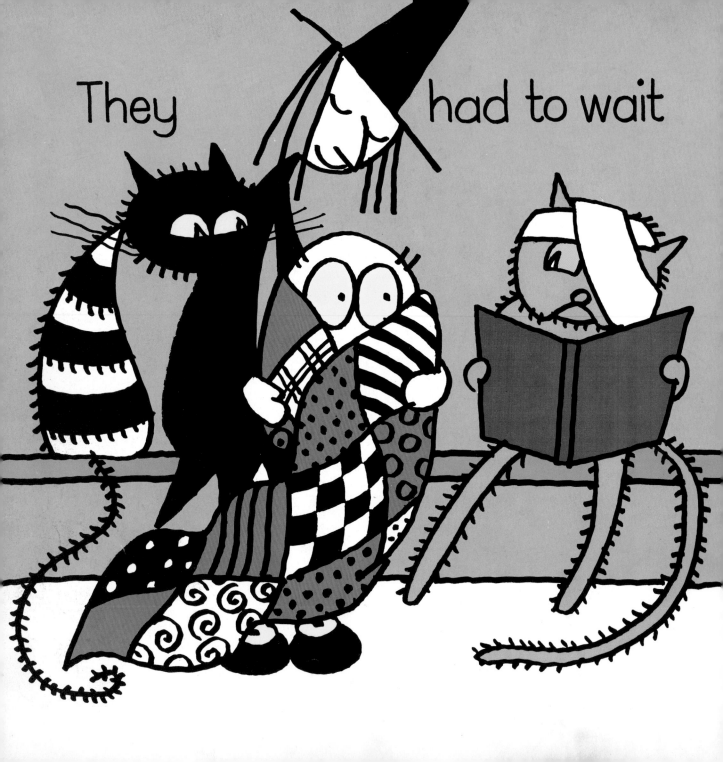

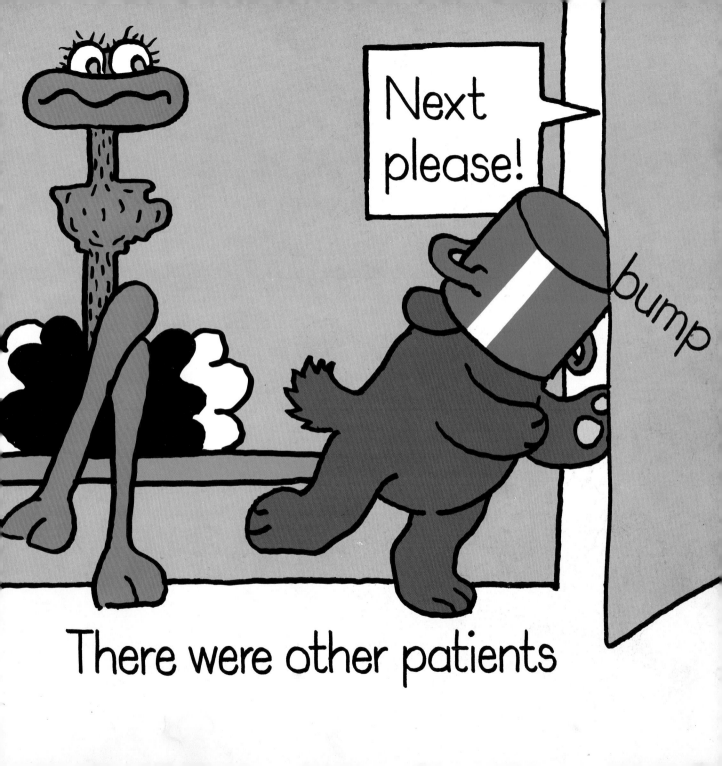

There were other patients

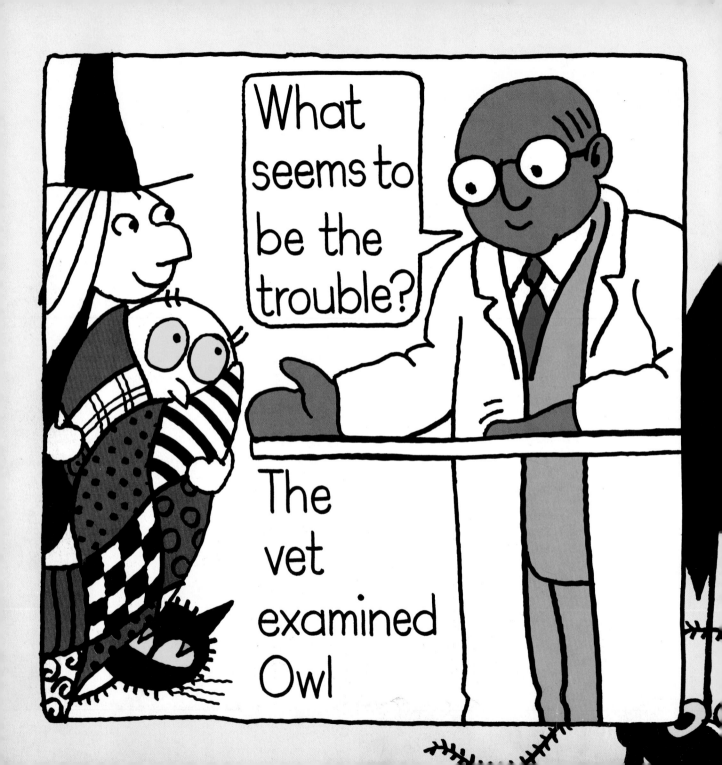

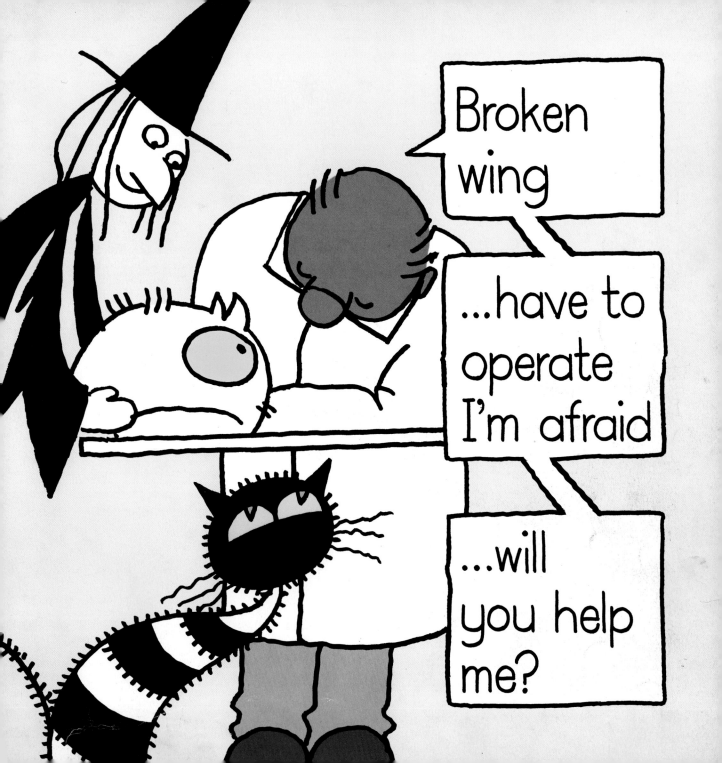

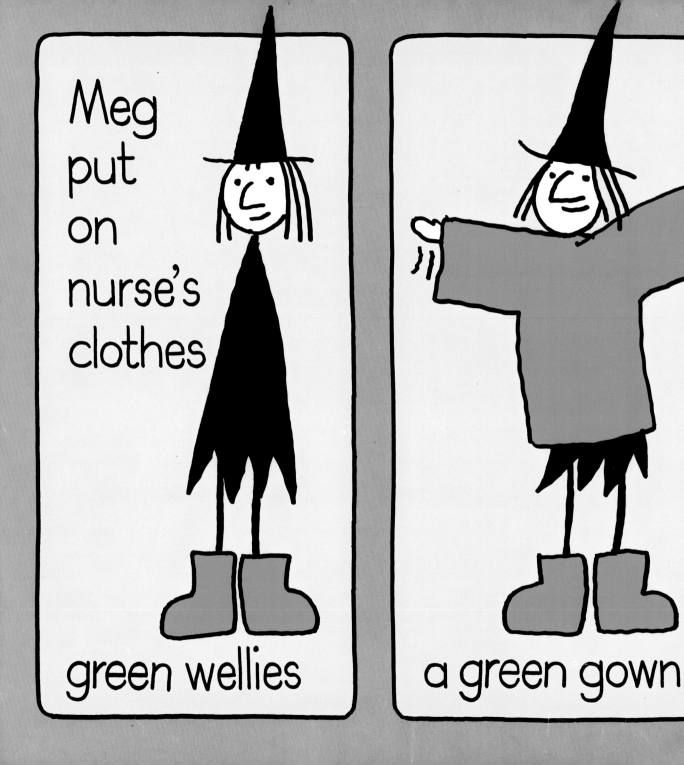

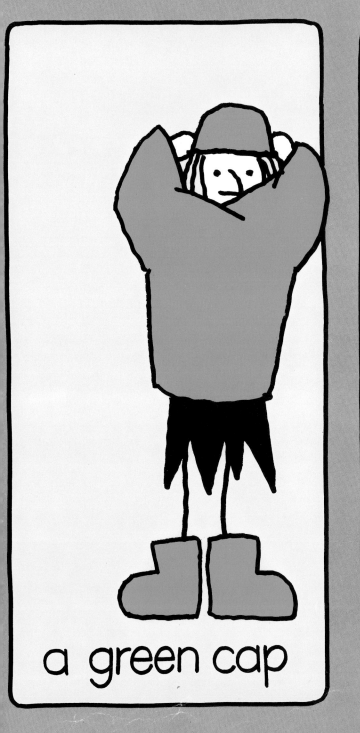

a green cap

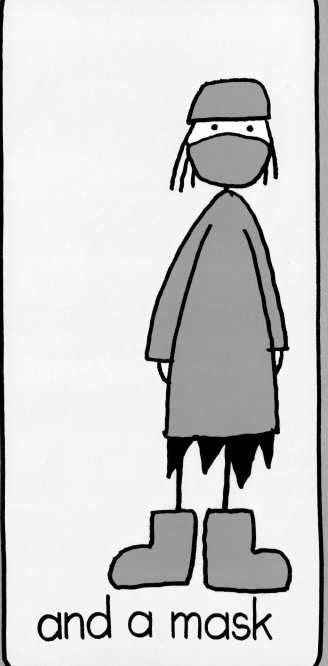

and a mask

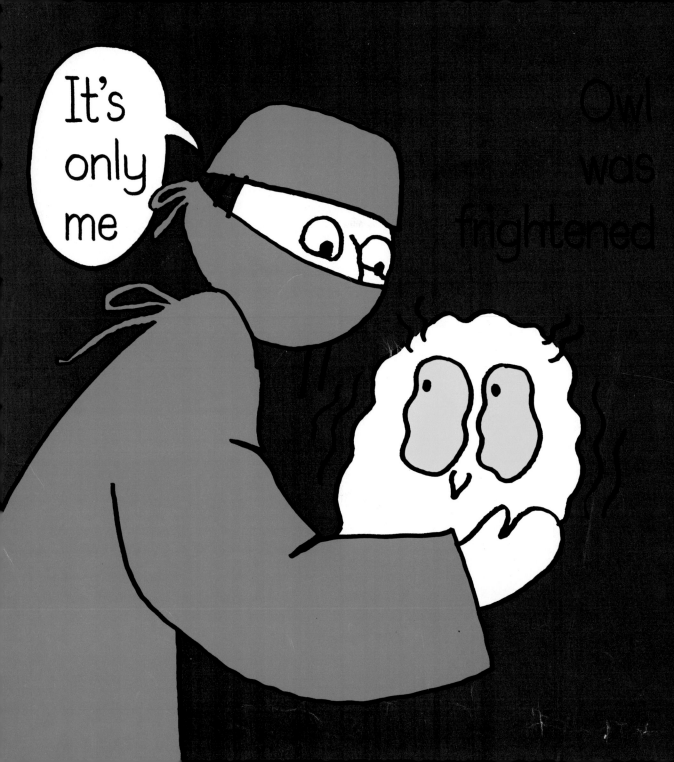

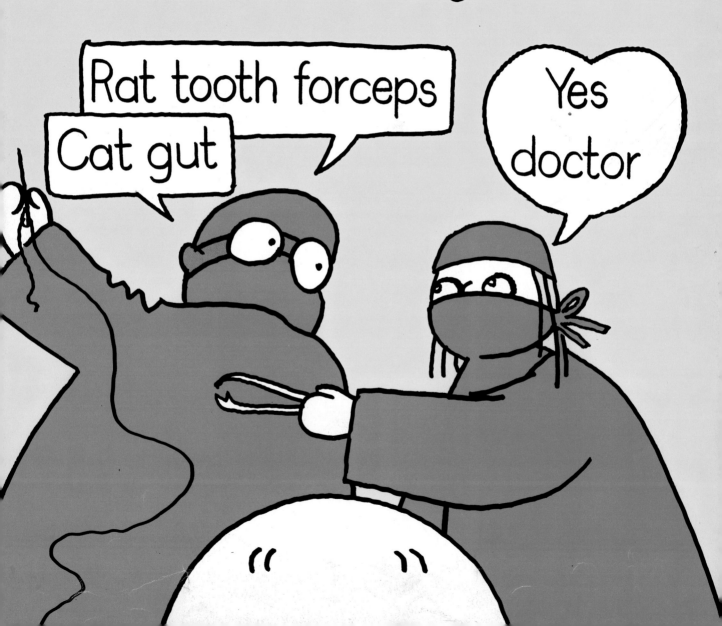

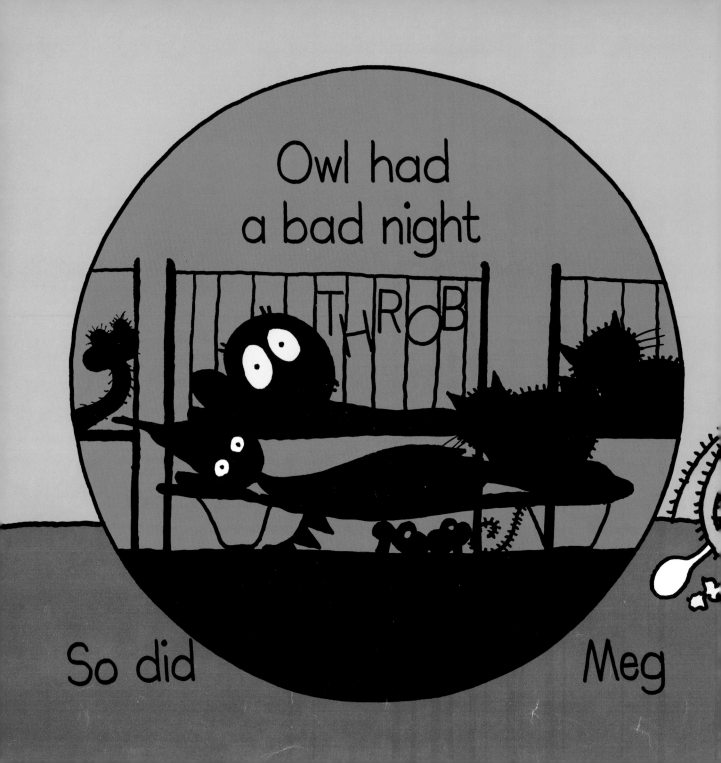

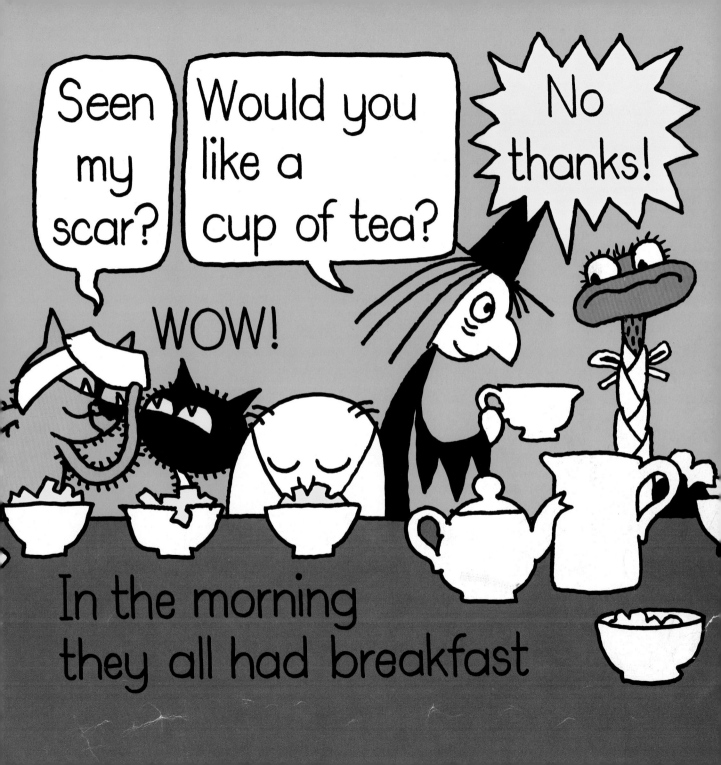

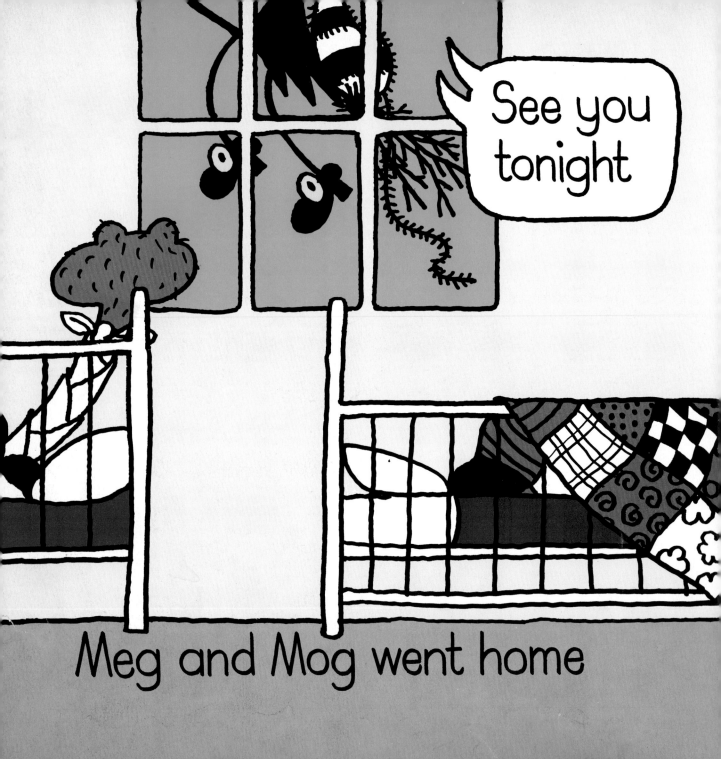

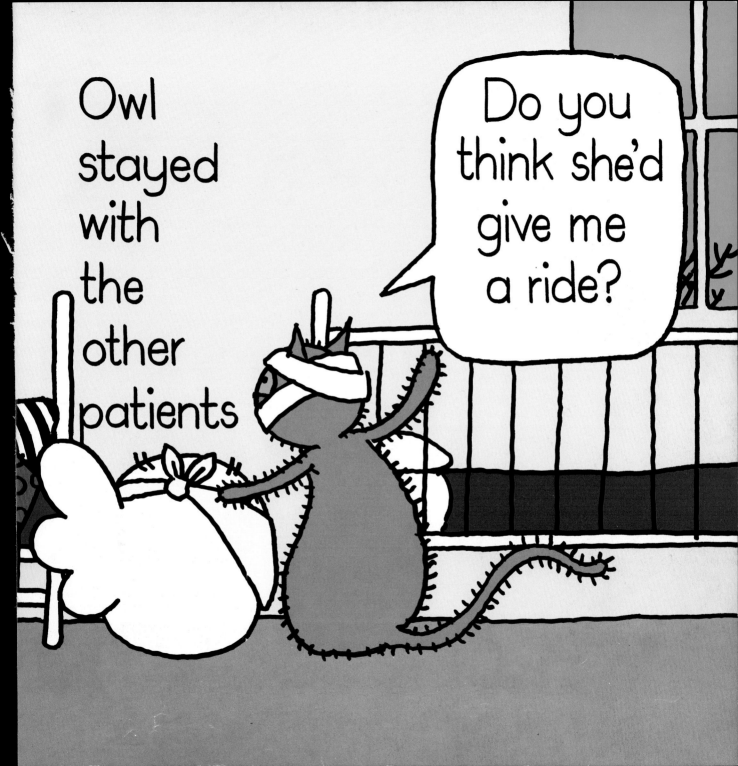

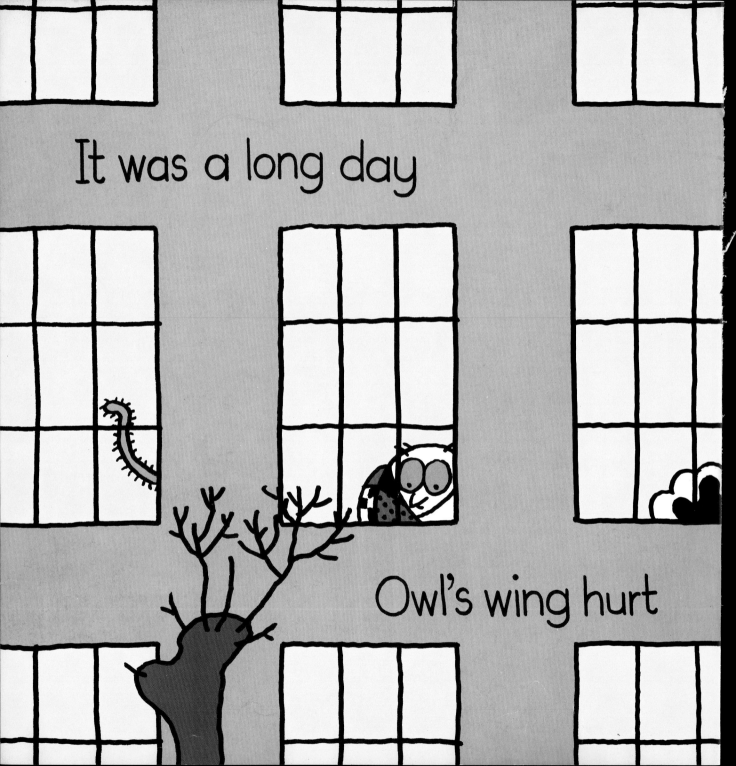

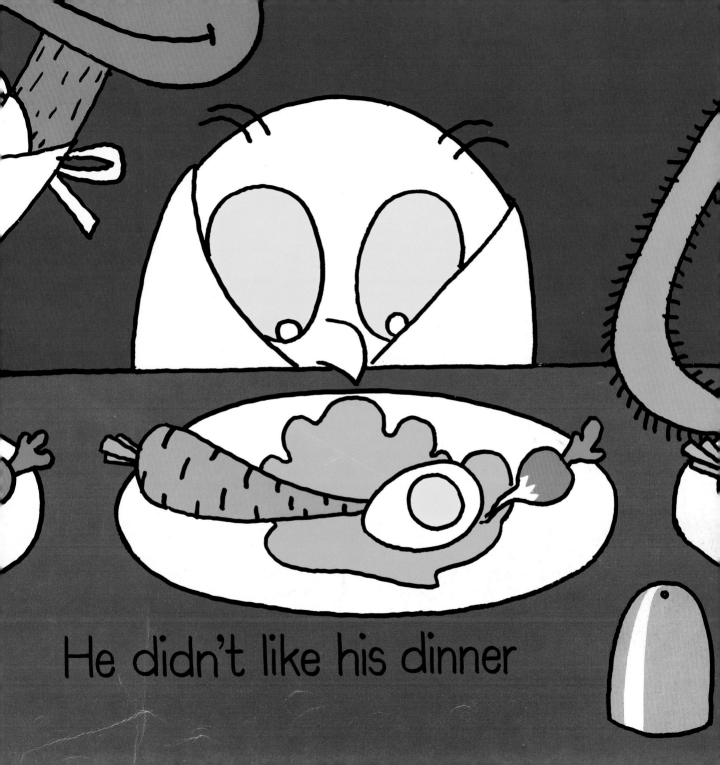

He didn't like his dinner

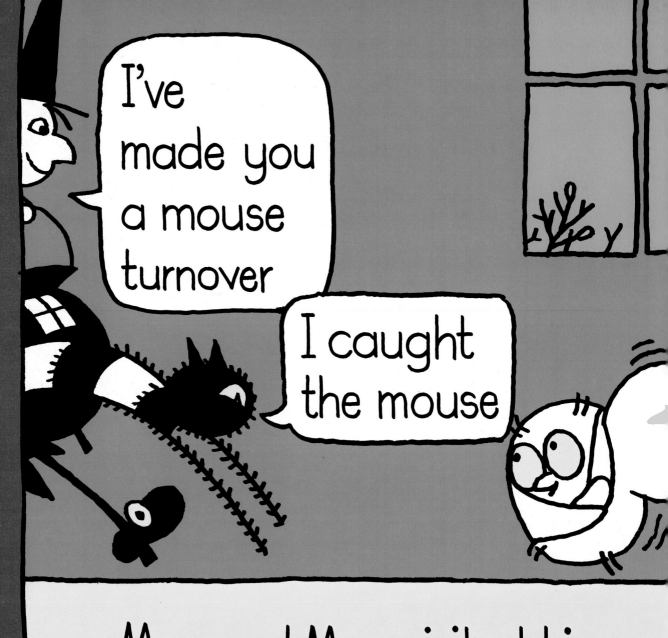

Meg and Mog visited him

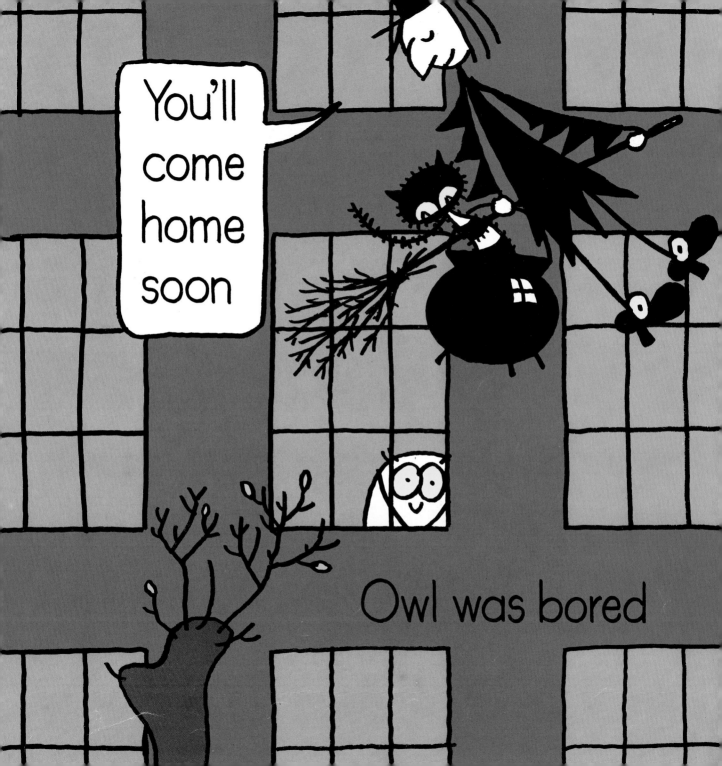

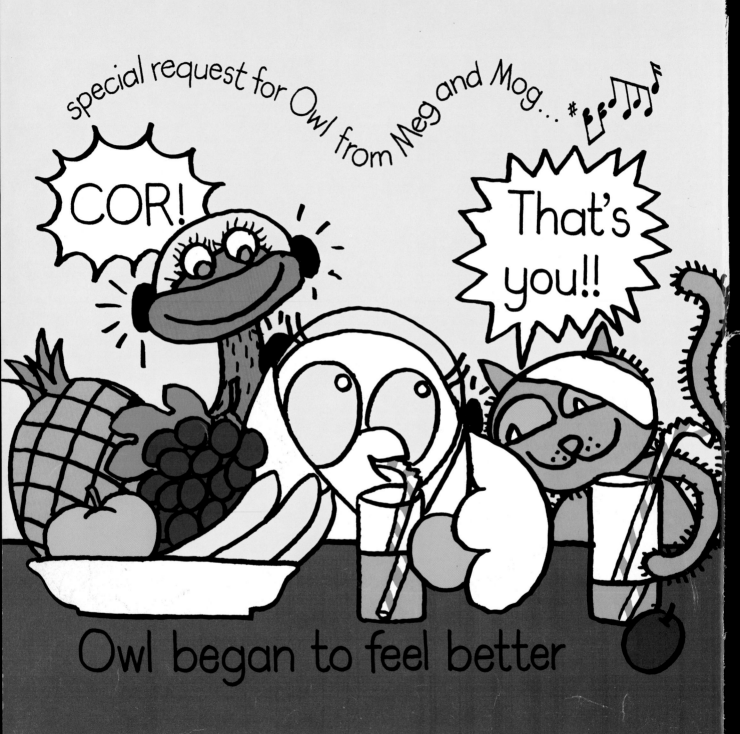

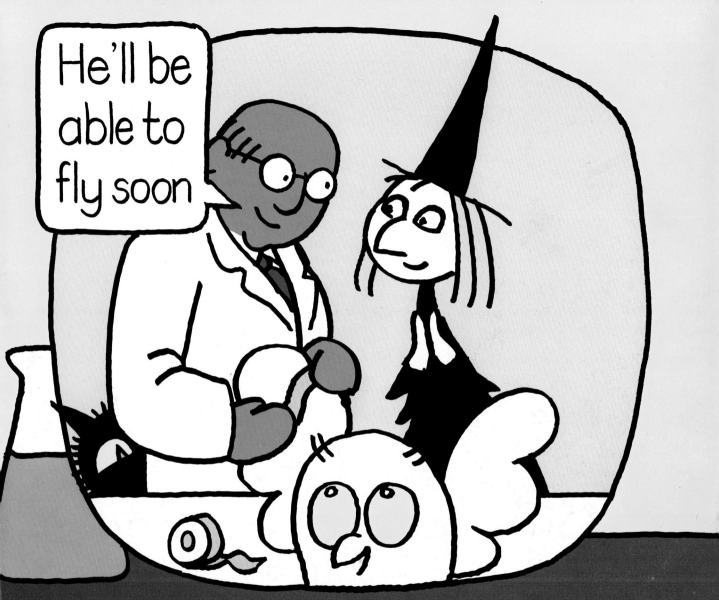

The vet looked at his wing again

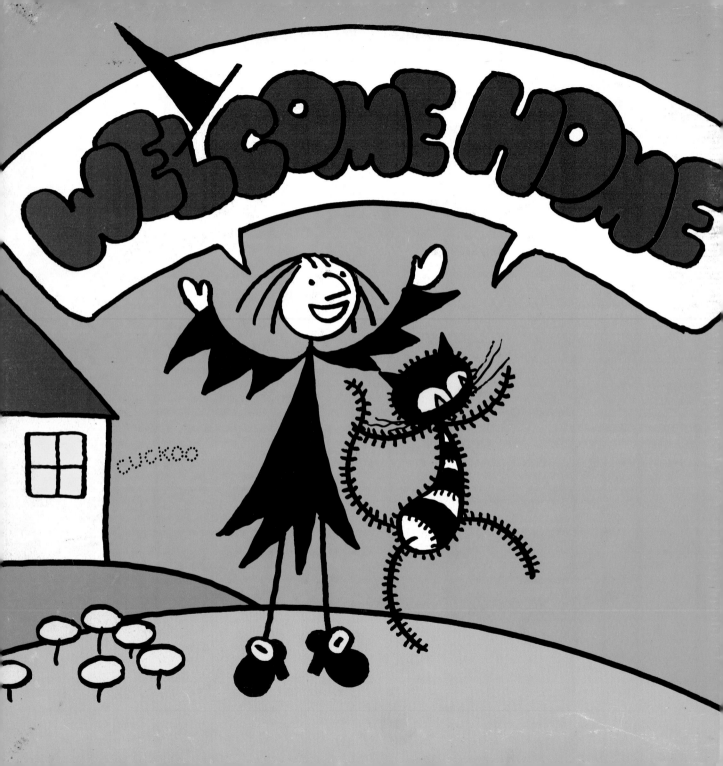